Three
on the Edge

Michael Loveday

V.

Published in the United Kingdom in 2018
by V. Press,
10 Vernon Grove,
Droitwich,
Worcestershire,
WR9 9LQ.

ISBN: 978-1-9998444-1-7

Front cover image: 'Laughing Clown at Bury Lake' © Lynda Bryant, 2018

Cover design © S.A. Leavesley, 2018

Printed in the U.K. by Imprint Digital, Seychelles Farm, Upton Pyne, Exeter EX5 5HY, on recycled paper stock.

V.

Contents

Denholm – Cause for Alarm

Gus – The Invisible World

V.

Martyn – Chewing Glass

V.

"Only connect!... Live in fragments no longer."
(E.M. Forster)

V.

"Somewhere in the hollows and spaces between our carefully-managed wilderness areas and the creeping, flattening effects of global capitalism, there are still places where an overlooked England truly exists..."

(Paul Farley and Michael Symmons Roberts)

V.

(I)   Denholm – Cause for Alarm

i. Lost Object

(Where are the fragranced pillows, where are the flying horses)
Denholm balances the square box on his palm, lifts the purple lid,
and inside, instead of hazelnut whirls and lemon crunches,
resting in the depressions of the plastic tray, are the fifteen pairs
of keys which used to open Gorgeous Gifts, no longer a going
concern (where are the Union Jack beard trimmers, where are
the tiger-print purses), he closes his eyes, fingers the keys, they
rattle in his brain, fifty years trading on Rickmansworth High
Street, Watford, Chorleywood, Bushey, St. Albans, places where
mother's business dug into Hertfordshire soil (find us the faux-
diamond ballerinas, find us the Spitfire key-rings); how he
cherished helping buyers turn panic to inspiration, and he drifts
back to the Rickmansworth storeroom, clambering through
stuffed cardboard boxes, the one-chair staffroom with its grown-
up magazines (go find the Hertfordshire egg-timers, go find the
invisible inks), and the smell of Grandma's daily gammon rolls,
how the shop became a home, how he memorised those cluttered
shelves (go get the coin-box skulls, go get the footballing pigs),
and how much he loathed the family party-trick, the loss of light
as they put the blindfold in place.

ii. Denholm Is Relying on Several Handsets for Incoming Calls, Each with a Separate Telephone Line:

(01923) 772433,

a beige touchtone, in the far left corner of the living room, on the *Harveys* coffee table over by the best sofa, mostly for Joan's relatives (some grime on the handset);

or 720348,

in the kitchen, cream and BT-supplied, with curled cord, also with advantageous large earpiece (though slightly uncomfortable), used for calls from Joan, sometimes she badgers while out on a spree;

or 775844,

in the bedroom, not yet relied upon, a scarlet-lipped handset (Denholm's jape), for emergencies, never know when it might prove useful, a midnight cold call from another time zone, perhaps;

or 770081,

a venerable dial-up, black, it's in the study, he revels in the clockwise feeling of his finger in each numbered hole, and savours the clicks as it springs slowly back into place, only now for Phil (his long-term friend), though previously for his mother, God rest her;

or 441119,

in the hallway, blue, or is it green, call it teal, a gift bestowed him by Phil, for new Rickmansworth residents with whom he wishes to bond, though for various reasons this number is rarely shared.

iii. PG Certificate

Denholm is leaning his neighbour's DVD of *The Trial* (the Welles version) against his bedroom window overlooking her garden. On the cover, a collage: Jeanne Moreau looks back nervily (off-guard at the sight of Anthony Perkins's steeled eyes, sculpted lips). Her hands flutter at her waist like sparrows. Behind them both, a second Perkins (shrunken), reaching up (far above his head), to turn the handle of an oversized door. The miniature man is on the tips of his toes, forever stretching (to open the door), what lies behind the door destined to remain unknown, and the door forever off-kilter, forever about to fall. Denholm hasn't yet watched the whole DVD (despite his passion for black and white), but as he balances the case on the sill, his decision to restructure his living space seems a crucial moment in his life, a harbinger of changes as yet unseen. He senses a quivering inside his gut, his heart, his blood, his liver, his right hand, his left hand, his groin, an eyelash, his nostrils; in the sliver of popcorn caught between his teeth, and the hairs in his ears, which his wife will doubtless pluck tomorrow.

iv. The Other Denholm

Apparently, Denholm's wife found him as a fledgling, listless and transfixed by the begonias in the back garden, flapping purposelessly, a punch-drunk startlement lingering in his eyes. She tells Denholm she's convinced he was attacked by the neighbour's cat, Rupert. It rendered him concussed, or brain-damaged – he seems a bit slow-witted. (Hence, she says, the name.) Her hard eyes thaw every time she speaks of him. She keeps him in a budgie cage, waiting for his strength to grow, hand-rearing him via socks soaked in milk. She wants her husband to build a bird-box on top of one of the garden sheds, and believes she is training the bird for adulthood – by beating her arms in front of him and leaping like an excitable tree frog into the air. Yet he seems to have decided his chances of survival are higher indoors, where milk is plentiful, the cat is banned, and Joan's empty palm is snug as a nest. Denholm the pigeon now vies with Denholm the husband for the position of Joan's confidant: at dinner times, he coos in response to her chirrups, patrolling the kitchen table while she cooks. (The real Denholm stalks him from the shadows, watching for proof of his filthiness.) He harbours a penchant for feta, and pine nuts, crushed and drizzled with olive oil. *Denholm, precious, are you remembering who you are? Denholm, my darling, will you ever fly again?*

v. Don't Sweat the Small Stuff

Denholm filches odd half-hours in the late afternoons, toiling in his second garden shed while Joan is distracted by the consolations of *Homes Under the Hammer*. Labouring on the sly requires him to be patient, and painstaking. He is gluing his model together, entirely from matchsticks (and, because of the matchsticks, it's taking a long time). His pockets rattle with matchboxes as he hobbles through town early on a Sunday morning, charting the landscape. Inside his overcoat sleeve, he smuggles the collapsible ruler that his mother handed down to him. The model seems accurate (St. Mary's Church, Watersmeet Theatre, the recycling tip, the Conservative Club, right down to the detail of buxom Faith's garden swing seat next-door). Yet heights and distances can only be approximated (he's no mathematician, and he's aware that ladders would be conspicuous in public (the church spire, for example, he suspects he's exaggerated by several feet)). A map is mere cousin of the territory, and Denholm is worried his task is less science than art; there's so much sheer guesswork involved. "Measuring is a form of possession," his friend Phil has claimed, though Denholm isn't certain what this means. Eventually, he intends to populate the model with tiny versions of the town's inhabitants, but he needs the nuts and bolts of its architecture bedded down beforehand, and the damned thing keeps shifting: shops and offices slip identities, new buildings repeatedly materialise. In this way, he's forever on a mission to catch up with reality, and the day of completion lies more and more remote. Thanks to Phil, the model bears a provisional title: *Rickmansworth – An Ideal Landscape*. In early evenings, Denholm crosses the sacred threshold of the shed (a boundary uncrossed by his wife), and stands within the silence of four wooden walls, studying his home town. Illuminated only by the rose-blush glow of a lava lamp, he looks down on thousands upon thousands of matchsticks – spliced, sculpted, bonded with blobs and threads of glue. This project must fill the bare, shrivelled garden that shelters at the heart of his life. He lowers himself into thought like he's floating in the Dead Sea. For a few minutes, he's alone, contemplating his masterpiece, and no one, no one can find him. [1]

---

[1] from *NOTES: Rickmansworth – An Ideal Landscape:* **Retail Inventory, 4th March 2012** [High Street recorded 9:00–9:34 a.m., Church Street 9:34–9:47 a.m., Station Road 9:50–9:58 a.m., Northway 9:58–10:02 a.m.]

Shops / Businesses beginning with 'D': Druids public house. [Honourable mentions: D.A. Long newsagent, F.L.Dickins off-licence.]

Shops / Businesses that can't be looked into [frosted windows / curtains / blinds / no windows etc]: Allday Recruitment, Archer Rusby Solicitors, Blaser Mills Solicitors, Chiropractic and Wellness Centre, Darlington Hardcastle Solicitors, Grosvenor Estate Agents, Heron Financial, IPA Financial Advisers, Landworth Electrics Ltd., Limegreen Design, LRG Insurance & Mortgage Brokers, Mace Express, Maharaja restaurant, The Osteopathic House, Paws and Claws, Seekers Recruitment, Soul Foods Group, Teco & Co, Trend & Thomas Estate Agents.

vi. The Heart of the River

The surface of the water wrinkles at the centre, and little rings expand to the edge. Denholm is hurling stones into the Grand Union – a Sunday stroll with Phil to catalogue new barges lining the canal. He's attempting to follow the path of a single wavelet, but his eye isn't good enough. (The ripples he causes can't be tracked: one glimpse of the whole bewilders the details.)

"It's romantic, don't you think?" Phil shows Denholm a photograph stored on his newfangled iPhone: an image of a swan pair, necks wound tight around each other.

"The kids bought me and Gwyneth a print," says Phil, "for our anniversary."

Denholm shrugs. "Could be the blur," he says, "but it looks to me like they're suffocating each other. There's no point counting all your chickens in one basket. I've got my shed. Joan has her plasma TV. And now she's got the other Denholm."

Phil coughs and flicks his rollie into the canal. He walks on in silence, and Denholm falters behind, passing a man painting pictures of the canal at an easel, and narrowboat owners renovating woodwork, until the Union Jack colours of the local Tesco appear on the opposite bank. A man nearly drowned round here last month, Phil calls back – a shelf-stacker dived in to save him while community support officers stood by hollering advice. Phil pauses to recall the new construction site for Churchill Retirement Living, at the far end of the High Street. Maybe Denholm would want a home there one day. Denholm nods: a sound choice.

By now they are nearing Batchworth Lock. They pass under the arch of London Road bridge. On one wall is a silhouette of a river barge, the figure of a woman at the helm, her hand poised on the tiller. Phil asks how Joan's moods have been recently.

"Talking of drownings," Denholm responds, "I fell over when wading in the Chess last week. The current is deceptive. If you stand at the heart of the river, it'll sweep you away."

vii. The Small Print

Very slow heart rhythm (heart block), cold hands and feet, worsening of Raynaud's disease (where your fingers turn white) and intermittent claudication (leg cramps which develop on walking), changes in the fat content of the blood, high or low blood glucose, blood disorders (with a tendency to bleed or bruise easily, or sore throat and mouth ulcers), tiredness, dizzy spells, depression, nervousness, confusion, mental disturbance, hallucinations, sleep problems, pins and needles, numbness of the extremities, weakness of the muscles, muscle cramps, painful joints, headache, dry mouth, feeling sick, being sick, diarrhoea, constipation, stomach cramps, fever, itching, scaly rash, worsening of psoriasis, blurred vision, sore eyes or conjunctivitis, impotence, Peyronie's disease (a condition in men affecting the penis), and (rarely) temporary thinning of the hair.

viii. Ceremony of Machines

Denholm and Joan follow the Croxley Boundary Walk, through tunnels of hedgerows and hawthorns. They emerge into a clearing: a shock of burgundy, olive and gold signage. Carter's Steam Fair is gathered on the Green, its annual ceremony of machines invading the mown grass. It's shrouded in rain-mist, deserted by the public after closing.

Here are the rock 'n' roll dodgems, Sensational Octopuses, Jubilee steam gallopers. The Paramount Chair-o-planes dangle on rusted chains from the top of the carousel. An il Tricolore ice cream van loiters at the edge of the Green. Vintage Scammell trucks litter the turf between rides.

The only person visible in the twilight is a pony-tailed man at a Test-Your-Strength stall. Rain has dampened the cigarette clenched like a reed between his lips, and he hunches over to fuss with synthetic dogs. Joan leads Denholm over to where the ritual beckons. The stall is decked in florid curlicues of Victoriana, flaunting portraits of Lloyd Honeyghan and Frank Bruno. A striped wooden hammer lies discarded on the grass. The bell at the top of the pole seems a long way up, its silver glinting like an object of worship.

"I'll do you a deal while I pack up – two pound for three strikes. Release your inner wild man. Or woman. You can win this, er, cuddly toy." He holds up the furred black dog; even the dog seems doubtful.

"My husband accepts your challenge," Joan says, apparently for her own satisfaction. She starts scouring her purse. "Denholm, do you have change?" She doesn't look up from the depths of her handbag.

Denholm withers. A relief to find his wallet empty. He offers up its bare leather as evidence to the man.

"How about you let him have a go anyway?" Joan asks as Denholm feels his stick-in-the-mud stance stiffen.

"Nothing free in this life," the man replies. Rain mizzles around them. He turns abruptly back to his dogs, leaving Denholm and his wife to face the silence of the fairground.

ix. Charred Wood

He's roused by the clatter of hooves and a furious rattling (he rubs his eyes, opens his window and squints): a wooden carriage and two horses galloping, galloping down Nightingale Road. Wherever they are going, they are going there urgently. The horses are pale grey; snorted breath steams in the air around them. The carriage is cluttered to the ceiling with engagement rings the size of life buoys, their cut gems flashing at him. A driver in white sits holding the reins, dark features obscured by a scowl, black braids streaming behind. She unleashes her whip and howls like a banshee with hell in her lungs: *Denholm, you boy-demon! Late! TOO LATE!!!* She buries a hand in her trousers, then flings a fistful of something at him. (A cloud-pale liquid splats on the bed sheets. With his frenzied wiping, it hardens to superglue.) Then, quick as this other has come, she is gone, gone with her clamour down the curve of the road, flames licking the back wheels and scorch marks patterning the tarmac. In the aftermath: a sweet odour of charred wood. Denholm lingers at the edge of waking, lured back by this night-spirit invading his slumber. On stiffened sheets, he drifts into darkness, unsettled, electric with desire.

x. *LOC*TITE Super Glue: Receipt #76/2012

"The Nation's No.1 Superglue[1], Strong & Flexible, Non Drip Gel, Instant Powerflex Adhesive"

Quantity: 3g

Purchased from: WHSmith Ltd., 74 High Street, Rickmansworth, WD3 1AJ

Time, Date: 15:49, 21st April, 2012

Price: £3.19   **Joan's 20% Privilege Card Discount:** -£0.64 **Net Price:** £2.55 (less than half of Araldite's price).

Glue Applications: China, Porcelain, Wood, Paper, Card, Rubber, Leather, Metal, "Most" Plastics. (**N.B.** Not Polyethylene or Polypropylene. Phil suggests these are thermoplastics, not thermosetting polymers. Interesting.) (**N.B.** Araldite can manage Fabric, Glass, Masonry, Dry concrete – superior range.)

Manufacturer Technical Services Department: Henkel Limited, 01442 278000

Hazards: "Bonds skin and eyes in seconds." (**N.B.** *Eyes? How did they research this?* Also, do <u>not</u> smell this glue again.)

Pros: Non Drip Formula (reduce mess on Rickmansworth project).

Cons: Not suitable for items that contain hot liquids or that will be wet in service (e.g. not on Joan's teacups).

Bonded Skin: In case of bonded skin, peel apart using soap, hot water and a blunt edge (e.g. teaspoon handle, don't tell Joan).

---

[1] "GfK RT UK Panel Market, Fast Act Glues, Value and Volume. Jan-Dec 2010." **N.B.** So this research is simply about sales quantity, NOT TECHNICAL QUALITY OF BONDING.

xi. O'Connorville

At Three Rivers Museum (two cramped rooms, kitsch cluttering the tables, a reassuring mustiness wafting through, like he's sniffing at a second-hand book), there are leaflets spread out on a rack, offered free to visitors. The wrinkled attendant explains that she wrote them all herself. Denholm respectfully selects one about Hertfordshire heroes (it is yellowing less than the others). Feargus O'Connor, leader of the Chartists, the country's first working-class movement: his Co-operative Land Company created an estate for Northern migrants, cottages built by local tradesmen, meagre plots of farmland to till.

Faded, photocopied images: a waistcoated man wears his hat tipped at an angle, right arm consoled by a shovel, left knuckles thrust at his belted waist. A wife and two children stand by him in sober clothes. The windows of his house are divided into small panes, the doorway flanked by rose bushes. The cottages each cost £100 to build, Denholm notes, which these days would buy only a Saturday summer evening in a Chorleywood B&B with the woman of his dreams. He shakes the leaflet straighter and reads on.

In 1847, O'Connorville began to welcome the shoemakers, tailors, doffers and weavers from the industrial North. Yet dreams of prosperity withered without rural skills. Within four years, of the thirty-five families who'd arrived, only seven remained.

Denholm slides the leaflet back into its plastic slot on the wall-rack. He turns to the window and peers along Rickmansworth's High Street. He sees those seven pioneers, rising in winter before daybreak, cheering themselves with rituals: boiling up water, smearing butter on slabs of bread, donning boots and thick overcoats, then leaving wives behind and heading through the doorway to pick nothing but stones out of Hertfordshire fields.

xii. Good Neighbours Make Good Fences

Denholm stands on the utility's flat roof, legs set shoulder-width apart to steady himself. He peers at his neighbour's garden: Joan is concerned about rats. There is the swing seat (a beige-cushioned sanctuary; and Faith is not rocking her body upon it). Today's heat is intense and his clothes are gathering sweat in unseen places. Perhaps he shouldn't be out in this weather. Still, he picks up his binoculars.

Pink petals skitter across sculpted gravel paths, a plastic bag from Iceland flaps in a chestnut tree, two police traffic cones huddle in the corner by her patio. No evidence of rats. But at the end of the garden, on his side of the lime-green fence, which the council has confirmed is Faith's responsibility (and whose wood he has watched slowly sag during her ten-year residence), is a small, unfamiliar rectangle of colour. How could he have overlooked it? He zooms in further: a playing card is stuck to the top of one plank. He clambers back down to investigate.

An old Top Trumps Marvel Super Heroes card: yellowed now, worn at the edges, and pinned by a gleaming nail to the wood. A silver Adonis poised on a surfboard, muscles rippling, right arm stretching for balance, left hand gesturing languidly skyward.

High o'er the roof of the World, he soars... the restless streaking Stranger from the farthest reach of space, whom Man shall call forevermore the Silver Surfer!

He looks back to the house, where the back of Joan's bobbing head can be glimpsed through the French windows as she scrutinises the TV, snacking on *Pointless*. A pot of tea brews on the trolley (Lady Grey, her favourite, no doubt). Up on the roof, their spindly TV aerial reaches out across slate tiles, steadfastly collecting its signals from the troposphere. Everything seems as it should be. He swallows, and slips the card discreetly into his pocket.

xiii. Onion Skin

He can't escape this: a teenager is chattering, bonding with her boyfriend by stroking his arm while twirling fingers through her pineapple hairdo. She pins a badge to the lapel of his navy school blazer – *No, teacher, I don't know the answers – and don't care –* and the boy guffaws. Their wide-eyed happiness is distressing Denholm, in front of the vegetable stand as he contemplates his wife.

It's true, Denholm questioned from the outset whether Joan was worth the gamble (in that leap year when she asked) as she waited for his no to emerge as a yes. But he's dimly aware, if he'd known, really known, how much marriage is one drowning person trying to push another under, he might not have risked it. He flees, too slow to escape; and she follows, too half-heartedly to snare him.

Denholm is wondering (in front of the onions) whether he's been worth the struggle; whether he should have negotiated a deal from the start, a platonic companionship cocooning them into old age, provided they'd granted each other freedom to roam. *The Daily Mail* at the Aquadrome, binoculars on the utility roof, evening rummagings in the murk of the shed, and neighbourly cream buns on Sunday mornings... Would that not, too, count as love? He is tolerably gratified, visualising this arrangement, even if the deal would have meant spending daytimes dutifully wheeling Joan around Rickmansworth Iceland. Yes, hunting down spirited children to moan at, for the shoddy state of their uniform (and skirts that are disturbingly short). Surely he sleepwalked into the wrong dream. Is he even awake yet?

He picks up an onion and turns it through his hands, studying its benign brown wrap of skin, wondering at the fumes contained within.

xiv. Our Lady Help of Christians

He slips beyond the black oak threshold, out of the downpour. Lurid, lime carpet greets him, and dark wood counterpoints the gleams of marble pillars. A formal feeling descends. Even though he's here by chance, he feels an urge to wander and look: it's what you do. Silence fills the nave, broken only by his footsteps. In a corner, candles are flickering, and he's drawn to the company of their light. He softens the end of one stem on the tongue of a flame then slides it into an empty holder. Shavings of wax curl off the base like some kind of soap. Is he now meant to ask a God for answers? Even as he quietens, all hope of conjuring a prayer fizzles out.

Behind the candles, *The Lives of the Saints* is splayed open and upright for viewing. Coloured light leaks onto the book from the adjacent window. His gaze swims unfocused over the text – tiny, insect-scribble descriptions of St. Cloud the Confessor. He touches one corner, and the page slowly turns under the tip of his finger. But he panics at the Virgin that he finds overleaf, scolding him for his instinct to tamper.

The page settles back. Denholm is paying attention now, and the rhythms of history beckon him: St. Cloud in 6th century France, orphaned, raised by his grandmother, renouncing the world, withdrawing himself into hermitage. Solitude, martyrdom, the ascetic who breaks the threads that bind: no one can live that way now. The world clutches too close, it floods us with longing. Denholm shakes his head, flicks the page over, then moves off to lose himself in the patterns of stained glass.

xv. Alarm

Now and then, Faith likes to switch on her smoke alarm in the middle of the night to wake Denholm. Summoning him next-door to read the electricity or kill her spiders just hasn't got his attention. She always gets going at about four a.m., because she wants to give Denholm one restful sleep cycle, timing her disruption such as to disarrange him no more than necessary. She leaves her windows closed and switches on the fan oven, dishwasher and tumble dryer simultaneously, since she has discovered that the combined increase in temperature is enough to trigger her temperamental heat-sensitive kitchen alarm, a method that she considers altogether more stylish than resorting to burnt toast. And, once this little monster has begun its relentless middle-of-the-night ear-pain, she leaves it screeching, ignoring the dismay of her only cat, Rupert, until the connecting alarms in the hallway and bedroom are also kicking off. The triple effect of these in the pitch of night is usually enough to rouse her dutiful neighbour. If he is sleeping quite soundly, she nudges him further by clattering chairs and slamming the stick of her broom against the adjoining wall, in a pretence of dealing with the blare. When she's heard his first tentative step down that creaking staircase, she removes all but a trace of make-up as if caught off-guard; tangles her braid bun into a just-out-of-someone-else's-bed look; then puts on her lilac slip, which she is certain is his favourite. She does this even though she is a happy widow now and Denholm is fifteen years her senior. She does this even though he struggles down those stairs at nights to get to her with his gammy leg. She does this because she can't resist her need for these performances: when his fingers press her buzzer and she swings the door open, she's always beguiled by that look on her own face.

xvi. Solitary Man, Or How He Tries to Save Himself, at 4:59 p.m. on Sunday the 13ᵗʰ May, with the Words of the Brooklyn Cowboy, Neil Diamond

3:39 p.m., he has arrived at *Intu*, Watford's antiseptic shopping mall, though he would concede it's expansive enough to maintain personal boundaries, and he's visiting to collect his vinyl copy (Special Edition) of *You Don't Bring Me Flowers* from HMV (Diamond has been a mentor ever since Joan dragged Denholm to see him perform (the same night Joan proposed), and to mark this frail musical coincidence, whenever Diamond gives a concert in London, Denholm aims to pay his respects, by attending).

3:44 p.m., all Denholm can think of is getting home for his evening ritual, cherishing his Diamond in his Second Shed during Joan's *Salvage Hunters* mindbath, when he finds it helpful, each week, to categorise the albums (by a variety of methods, depending on the most reliable system for that particular week, which may be alphabetical (it's possible to order the world), chronological (ultimately, over time, the individual can grow, learn and develop, albeit sometimes via false starts and culs-de-sac), or even (always the trickiest judgement) by extent of Diamond's visible chest-hair). But however Denholm structures them, Diamond's albums remain an enduring enigma (their meaning, their manly passions, and Joan's devotion towards them), one that Denholm is determined to solve.

3:48 p.m., he's still waiting in line at His Master's Voice; of course Denholm's fear of the world's wide web inhibits him from internet shopping, so he's resorted to ordering via the beige living room telephone, for as long as this terror exists, and he visits the store monthly, collecting whatever has arrived, and today is the second Sunday of the month, that's what suits Denholm best, the second Sunday; and then it is 4:24 p.m., and he's disconsolate on the 320's stop-start (via the backstreets of Croxley's two-storey semis), returning without his copy of *Flowers* (he should have *emailed in advance*), and bearing only a sorry clutch of Engelbert Humperdink CDs.

4:55 p.m., as he's ambling down Nightingale Road, then turning to enter the driveway of his home, Denholm is jolted by the sight of it, and he stops to study this property that he shares, as if he had never actually lived there, even though he has done so for the last thirty-four-and-a-half years; and now he is noticing flaking white paint on exterior walls, he is noticing fake Tudor beams, and leaded-light windows, he is noticing variegated brickwork, and a black swing gate, and a lawn unmowed, and a rusting garden roller abandoned upon it, and all this as for the first time, as if this building did not house him and his wife, but contained only the lives of apparitions half-glimpsed and unknown.

4:59 p.m., Denholm is propping himself up against the gate, poised at this homesick boundary, and he's thinking about his neighbour Faith, the last thing she said to him, what did it mean, and what on earth should he do? If he lets her, she'll engulf him. He feels his whole panicked existence unspooling before him like cassette tape chewed up by a machine, and now he is recalling songs, looking for answers, a sequence of favourites, and he's heard Diamond perform all these live: *Two-Bit Manchild, I Am... I Said, The Long Way Home, Say Maybe, I've Been This Way Before, Amazed and Confused, Home is a Wounded Heart, Captain of a Shipwreck, Don't Look Down, Solitary Man.*

(II)   Gus – The Invisible World

i. St. Mary's Churchyard, January

A community of stones stands upright, bold as poked tongues, while the bare and level white accumulates. A holly bush takes shelter; snowflakes settle on its leaves, little miracles that gleam then fade, gleam then fade. Before long, the green is overwhelmed by the snow's immaculate veil.

In the midst of this ground: the flat, shadowed form of a slab, a doorway of sorts. Gus might search for a handle to pull, to open a route into the earth. But the surface is plain – and nearly expressionless, except for a deeper darkness at its boundary, where the rim of the shape attempts to cut the covering snow, to break through to daylight.

ii. Bury Lake, February

His wife's voice accompanying him, he circles the lake as breezes drag shadows over the surface.

The water is troubled by a motorboat; waves lap at the land's edge, nudging rotten branches lodged in the dregs of leaves, pulling, calling them back.

Honour me now I'm gone – companionship's the cure. Don't fashion yourself an abyss, don't spiral within.

Sailors scurry across the lake, answering the winds. One dinghy flips, the pilot disappears beneath, only – as the vessel spins – to emerge, breathless, hugging the upturned keel.

iii. The Chess, March

From the riverbank, he sees the fish – five of them, not moving. Or rather, they keep still by trilling their tails against the current.

They're swimming where the shadow of a bridge leans onto the water, and never stray far, though sometimes they lift themselves, gulping at air – something on the surface, maybe an insect, a leaf.

The following lunchtime they're gone. Gus is ready to turn when one of them noses from under the bridge, nudging its way out of darkness. Its tail keeps ticking, moving without moving, a man in a pool treading water. He crumbles off part of his sandwich and tosses it into the river. The piece is too big and it bounces away from the snapping mouth, floating downstream.

He returns the next day with gifts from the pet store – pungent pellets like mouse droppings. He throws them in clusters at the water. The fish summon themselves out of hiding to nibble at the surface, darting about as pellets catch currents and flow towards the bridge. They're part-coloured, with markings on their sides, drabness mimicking the brown-green river.

He goes back daily. Some of these fish are three feet long, thick with muscle, too fat to put a hand around, feverish with power as they pulse in the water.

They swim closer each time, shadows rising from shadows, closer to where he stands on the bank. He can't bear to see how they need him.

iv. Stockers Farm, April

Gus kneels in the meadows. He's had to cross the lock and slip through a gate to get here. It is early and the earth is damp as he places his palm on the ground. He looks ahead through field after field: a few horses in pastures, unknown crops, and then on the Rickmansworth side of the canal, the lakes sprawl south, water massing into the distance.

A robin's song meddles with his thoughts, yet he's glad to keep listening. It is the song of the beloved. He dredges up words, willing them into prayer: *Whatever happens, wherever loss takes me.*

He's falling: inside and beyond. The tall houses of the trees tell him to hear the bellow of God within. There is only silence. He closes his eyes, sees dandelion clocks spill from his hands.

v. Stockers Lake, May

At the signpost to Springwell and Inns Lakes, he switches off his phone, slips through the Wildlife Trust gates, and strides along the muddy track, fields to his left-hand-side and river to his right. The Colne is fast-moving here, but soon it's slowed by a curving route and turns sluggish. The trail is lined with nettles, dock leaves, and cow parsley pullulating in great bursts and crowding the way. Scarred desire paths split from the main track, meandering through the grassy spaces. Felled trees hang low across the water – by one brook the hacked limbs of an ash are bent double, sagging under the weight of the yellow metal container discarded and propped upon its back. A black tyre hangs from a rope, swaying in the breeze like a pendulum.

Within a few yards, signs of industry begin to appear on the far side of the river – glimpses of urban life obscured by thickets of hawthorns and nettles. In a car park, trucks and lorries wait to be rescued from disrepair; wagons are stained with algae; the backs of ribbed and rusted metal boxes poke through green leaves. Further on, amidst the hedgerows: plastic sheeting; a rain-stained Rank Xerox container; an orange row of gas canisters; a solitary traffic cone. It's as if human striving has yielded to the forces of nature, and allowed itself to be overrun – a land that even time has abandoned.

An engine whirrs, jolting the fantasy. A few paces later, wild becomes feral, bushes and trees thickening, consuming all proof of metal and machine. The ghost of a tree emerges, branches reaching across the river like the twisted claw of a giant; the only thriving thing the vine that's killed it. Then the river winds away, nettles and cow parsley overwhelming the path that leads him to Stockers Lake.

Over Gus's head comes the creaking of a mute swan pair, necks taut, as straight as clarinets; their shadows follow too, beating across the grass. He traces the swans' course over the quarter-mile of water, to a sky mottled with clouds and the low sun maintaining its gaze like a bloodshot eye. What would his wife have made of this moment? Everywhere he looks, she is an almost-presence meeting his thoughts. There's a veil between him and the world that will not lift, and to tear it down seems a betrayal. Why is it still not consolation – witnessing these swans, these shadows, this sky?

vi. Bury Lake, June

Lashed by the wind, the lake is a sullen grey. A miry backwash, flecked with pale scum, laps and soughs at the perimeter. The mute swan pivots, dips its neck to dredge... Is there nourishment under the surface?

Root-slime, mud-leaf.

Maybe the swan is a mind fathoming for answers. Gus sees a house trying to empty every box of junk from its own cellar.

vii. Batchworth Lake, July

Early one morning, Gus walks past the empty children's playground and over the bridge across the Colne. He carries his Polaroid, photographing swans, coots, and moorhens. He waits for their outlines to develop in the summer light, soothed by their journey from vagueness to certainty.

A whitish mist hovers over the first lake, and he stops to study two mallards idling on the jetty. The male twists its neck back to preen its feathers, supervising the female sidelong from one eye. From the edge, the female looks out over the lake, though it seems there is nothing in particular to gaze at.

Beyond the haze that crawls across the water, an island glowers in the distance, covered with the heavy green of trees, and deepened with shadows that seem darker and more solid than the trees themselves.

After a long time of stillness, he turns his mind again to the mallards. The female has slipped into the water and now moves off, rippling the surface as it glides away. The male seems to observe a respectful pause, then drops into the lake and follows towards the island.

viii. Springwell Lock, August

Reeds rise from the floor of the canal, slim, billowing in the murk.

Has anyone ever managed to settle here? There is no gatekeeper's cottage. The bridge carries cyclists escaping towards Harefield. At times, a slow silhouette might trail its length, heading for Garrett Wood. Two older men are strolling down the towpath, talking and looping stones into the canal as if they were children. Gus lingers by the arch, watching a second bridge waver in the mirror beneath.

Now the lock, like a bank vault, longs to open. Boatmen spread palms on the beams that span the canal, ready to lean their weight. Gade, Chess and Colne are dammed against wooden gates, white noise spitting through sluices.

What is a gateway but a history of exits? The lock has documented them within the gloss and slime of water stains. Liquid in a blocked sink, so the level climbs, until the markings of the past have disappeared.

ix. Town Ditch, September

Five corpses float at the surface. Carried in the water is a dark sludge that seems to be silt: when he dips his hand, the sludge smells only of earth.

The next day many more litter the ditch. He gives up counting. They bob in the slow current, spinning as they snag against branches and leaves.

He looks closer, sees others, alive, rising to the surface, their gills beating for breath amid the black silt. Chubs, bullheads, minnows, roaches. Glinting silver scales, sandy-yellow blotches, flecks of gold, orange. The dead ones float flat on their sides.

He shivers. The bare eyes stare up, gawping blindly at him.

x. Batchworth Lake, October

The blackbird's darting back and forth sews a clot in his mind.
Somewhere within this, a question festers – a matter of faith.

Could he heal without forgetting?

A yellow beak's pulling the blood-clot tight. The bird reels at
speed, wingbeats tugging at threads no one else can see.

xi. Garrett Wood, November

He watches its eyes: never at peace, not even in the dark; it lifts an unsleeping head from the coils of its rest.

He watches its movement: it sidles and weaves, over the earth.

He watches its loneliness: in the long grass it hides, curled as a sea-rope, biding its time.

He watches it speak: a half-formed spitting from its jointed skull.

He watches it hesitate: soon it will slough off its worn self, slip a changed shape out of the slack of its own dead mouth.

xii. Stockers Lock, December

Everything seems stilled into silence, but for the river hissing through the lock. A pair of horses angle towards each other; they graze the meadow which unfolds itself for the sun's touch, fog clinging to the hills.

The horses are faithful to being alone. They bow their heads as their tails flick defiantly. One crow lifts from a tree, pulls itself across the skyline.

Gus believes in neither the horses nor the crow. He wills it to be the horses who rescue him. The water keeps breaching the gate, and he eyes the rising canal.

(III)   Martyn – Chewing Glass

i.

To Martyn, Rickmansworth resembles a delicate wrist-watch, with a built-in tendency to lag behind the beat of time. A case in point: he is at Watersmeet Film Club, on a rain-soaked Thursday afternoon, and the movie is *Eat Pray Love*, screening a full two months after its London release. Most of the seats in the theatre are empty. Aside from a large tub of butterscotch ice cream, his only company is a smattering of female pensioners. Wispy white hairdos illuminate the dim hall as he finds his way through the temporary plastic seating. Martyn is having an off-day. He's chosen this film because he knows Anja likes the story: a woman who travels to India to find herself. But in truth the woman is searching for The One. The movie is full of turns and disappointments—and just when the heroine seems about to settle on her choice, the projector slips its reel and the screen runs to blankness. Outside the theatre afterwards Martyn loiters, wondering where on earth he's drifting to. Maybe The One he's destined for doesn't live in South West Hertfordshire after all. On the wall is a giant poster for Aladdin—the next Watersmeet panto. He dragged Anja and Rob to Cinderella last year. He slinks back home in the cold and wet, with just one wish for his jinxed magic lamp.

ii.

It's 4 a.m. Not yet light. He wakes from the sweat of a dream. Now he spreads Anja's leotard across his closed eyelids, and loses himself in her forbidden image. He did experiment for several months, but he found—mostly to his disappointment—that if there is one thing which can cauterise his mind—enough to let him slip from consciousness at this hour of the night—it is the leotard.

iii.

Martyn lies still until the cobweb of a dream has lifted—
something about being naked in a church and his dead mother as
priest offering all manner of Communions. He tries not to think
about it—behind closed eyelids, he listens for the morning.
Already the lorry reversing outside is an alarm that chides him
for remaining in bed; already the roadworks' pneumatic drill
asks *why don't you find a proper job, you workshy tyke?*
Somewhere—deep beneath the sockets of his eyes—a familiar
ennui is working itself to the surface, and he begins the old
negotiation with this other self, deploring the need to peel back
the covers. He surveys the terrain of the day: ahead of him lie the
Watford Observer, the manifold betrayals of the canvas, and
Loose Women studied from the comfort of the sofa. His routines
are a deep-sea dive in a copper helmet and weighted boots:
labouring at the bottom of the ocean, beneath currents, moving
at half-pace in the murk. Will his air supply be cut? He's been
down here for what seems like too long. Someone has stolen his
diver's watch. He's forgotten what daylight looks like.

iv.

Decapitation by bread knife! Gluten-free beer bottle in the eyeball! At Waitrose checkout, Martyn often startles himself—using supermarket items for imagined acts of violence against other customers. At least, he was startled *at first*. These days he comforts himself—it's his way of purging the silent rage organically produced by the British when queueing. As long as he's releasing his demons this way, people are less likely to come to physical harm. Corkscrew through the back of the hand! Tin of three beans in the teeth!

v.

Each time Anja leads a yoga session at Loudwater Farm, he falls a little deeper into the madness. He wanders through corridors, dazed and bewildered, lost in a warren full of agile temptations. Anja advises him on his breathing in one-to-one sessions after the main class, drawing tiny, mysterious diagrams in her notebook—which only make him puff a little quicker than he should. And then there is the tremulous, slow voodoo of her speech—seductive as the drip of manuka honey from a spoon. But of course Anja is no siren teasing him, she is only his Penelope, weaving her shroud, and waiting for him to finish his Odyssey. It is these others who are the sirens, resplendent in lycra. So he tightens his straps, glad for the sturdiness of the mast, and rows himself home down Chorleywood Road.

vi.

Rob's post-dinner arm-wrestle challenge seems a test waiting to be failed, though Martyn feels obliged to allow it. The first bout lasts longer than expected—is Rob toying with him?—then descends into chaos. Rob surely lifted his elbow, and cocked his wrist to gain advantage. They tumble onto the sofa, Martyn's torso in Rob's bear-grip. Biting his hand seems the only escape. Martyn's teeth are bared, then Anja re-enters the room, and the boys start dusting themselves down, laughing and back-slapping. They return to nurse their respective *London Prides*, and as they sip a silence descends—a vacuum that Anja must fill.

vii.

He invents ex-lovers and recounts fantastical backstories to Anja—telling her these women live on as ghosts in his bedroom. It might manifest as no better than a cliché, except for the tokens he clings to, summoning defunct relationships in the dread hours—the jewel-encrusted hairbrush—the rosary—the one-eyed panda—the fountain pen with the split in the barrel.

viii.

Martyn's Grand Union landscapes are an ecocentric project—the artist-self tamed, its genius tethered to acts of witness. But a little wildness must be let loose on every canvas—to pierce the viewer's eye. Martyn directs Rob's glance past the mute swans lifting from blackening water. Gunmetal clouds loom, wind rips through snow-covered hawthorns. And here, a terrier pees on the houseboat *Lovers' Knot*—while the balding boat-owner dotes on his roses.

ix.

In Anja—he doesn't yet tell her—he's found the companion all men surely crave: a guardian-god of his secrets, magnifying mirror to his better self, and match for his lost mother's perfections. She's his kindly care-bringer, and might as well be his twin, so mousy-fine is her hair, so hazel her irises, so pale her complexion. One shadowed glimpse of her in the evening window glass—how devilishly beautiful he looks.

X.

The Halloween cake, populated with bloodied, severed limbs made from icing sugar, doesn't seem like the most appealing use of a window display. Nevertheless, he needs some chamomile respite at Cinnamon Square—he's definitely not heading to the Tate Modern for Ai Weiwei's 'Sunflower Seeds'—not after wasting his own morning at the easel. From his point in the queue, he spies Rob's shaved head in the courtyard but isn't in the mood—it's a no-talk day—a glass-mouth day. Martyn slips past the open window towards the refuge of interior tables in one of the low-ceilinged rooms. He sits, and hides behind his book—*I am an Other*—eyes wandering all over the page and unable to focus. If Rob spots him and wants to walk the plank of speech, Martyn will inform him that he has to work. He's so pressed for time these days—not least with his painting, which he nurtures in adversity, and which fills his days like a giant cactus flower.

xi.

Martyn attempts to survive the narrow gauntlet of the High
Street, dodging other pedestrians peering into glinting charity
shop windows; but a woman from St. Mary's community group
emerges from Age UK, clutching a giant white rabbit under one
arm. Recognition brings the recurring dose of fondness and
shame—memories of dabbling—before Anja arrived—with
secret and misplaced lusts. *How is she?* he feels compelled to
ask—and then dredges up more when she doesn't move on—*Are
her moods ok?* She answers—all seems well, though her therapist
has impregnated her by mind control. She's on her way to The
Lakes to meet him and bring him this gift. He's a shrink at
Shrodells Unit—but it's early days—and he's a shy man—so
they're not telling anyone. Already the prospect of her departing
tantalises Martyn—like a prize under a fairground grabber.
Perhaps she'll sense it. How is he for romances? Still throwing all
his effort into his paintbrush? The devil makes lovers of idle men,
she winks, melting back into the crowd.

xii.

The clockwork vampire teeth—Anja's Halloween gift—rest impatiently on the studio table. The scarlet gums match the plush of the curtains framing the window overlooking the communal garden—a tightly manicured lawn in the shadow of trees that line the canal. Martyn refers to the communal garden only irregularly for inspiration. He continues to paint his long-gestating sequence of canal landscapes. A man kneels in the fields of Stockers Farm, eyes closed, seeming to pray. A horse stands nearby, mane lifting in the breeze. Every few minutes Martyn winds up the teeth, then waits as their chattering dwindles to silence. Click, click—a daub of blue. Click, click—a dab of black.

xiii.

To join the London Olympics as proxy hero, Martyn intends to complete two thousand and twelve laps of Bury Lake. He's not running for charity—it's a piece of performance art, and he'll be running backwards with a paintbrush as a baton that he'll pass to nobody. He'll draw two thousand and twelve sketches of the seasons as they change round the lake, documenting blossom, bloom, leaf-fall then bareness. Rob will monitor his progress—he must average five or six laps per day. Martyn is bursting with power, and pleased with his own ambition—he promises to invest in new trainers each time he loses his grip. He's not sure he can keep it up—though Rob cheers him by saying if there's any exercise that suits him, it is surely running.

xiv.

The casings of the avocado sit on a plate. He's scraped them dry for his latest still life—they sit there looking like a womb split in two. He turns one over to touch the scabbed skin where it tapers, fingering it gently. Now he craves something illicit in this evening heat. He rolls the damp fruit-stone over his palm, savouring its otherness. Grip and let go. Grip and let go—it wobbles across the lifelines.

xv.

Martyn nobly crawls out from under the dreaming cherry tree. His big hand snaps off a branch covered with leaves, to hide his masculinity, then he charges at the unknown women as if he were a mountain lion compelled by starvation—confronting the tempest with a visceral belief in his powers—eyes lit with fire— hunting down cows or sheep or deer—even the animals most carefully protected by their owners. And so Martyn—though starkly naked—is driven to rage at these women with their mesmerising braids of hair. But he looks so filthy—encrusted with sea-salt—that the whole flock scatters itself in all directions along the wildness of Batchworth Lake.

xvi.

E-G-G-S-E-G-X-S—in glimmering candlelight, the planchette shifts under Anja's and Rob's fingertips, while Martyn balks from a corner at the spirit world's hollowness. Either the pair are communing with the ghouls of disgruntled poultry farmers or Rob's wooo-aaahh ghost-noise is as credible as Ouija boards get. Anja's thigh shakes impatiently under the table's improvised green baize. She puts a hand over Rob's mouth, insists upon silence in which to murmur incantations, then quits when the candle sputters out—demon mindfuckery, she says. A spooked Rob declines his turn; at last Martyn's fingers partner Anja's at the board, with Rob relegated to a place in the shadows. Close by her, Martyn is inhabited by a new mood. He wills their hands to conjure a truth—about love, or lust, it matters not. *G-N-N-F-H-M-N-F-F-H*. He memorises consonants in the aftermath, fervently scribbling them down, hunting, hunting for blessings, refusing to stop.

xvii.

At dinner with Anja and Rob—in Tamarind Thai—Rob is devouring tom yum soup, slurping so disgustingly that Martyn is losing his wits. Along with small talk and cheeriness, soup slurping is Martyn's weak spot. He's meant to remain charming but all he can think about is grabbing Rob's neck and thrusting his blunt head hard into the bowl of bobbing prawns. He's tempted to draw Anja's attention to it subtly, so they can begin to conspire over the lack of civility. Instead, he digs his thumbnail into his index finger with force—displacing one distress with another—then confirms his own unagitated demeanour in the glass of the mirrored adverts hanging on the walls. His own broth arrives and Martyn puts on an exquisite performance of immaculate silence. Rob's slurping has finally stopped, but the mere idea of its return obliterates calm repose—a pea under a mattress.

xviii.

Easel, palette, subject—his glance is shaped by everything he sees. A shade more pink required. No, *vermilion*. Each time he tries to fix her in paint, her subtleties master him. There, that laughter-line to the left of her lips—it pricks at him like a needle. Anja can never be brought to the canvas—something, somewhere, misses the mark. The oils he dabs on, he scrapes off the next day, accumulating dry residues in little hills at his feet. And so he commits to more versions of her. A kind of entrapment—and yet—that pool of shadow held by her collar bone, her earlobes, that ladder running the length of her thigh... Today he regulates his gaze through an abstract approach—translating her body into fixed lines and geometric forms. So what if all that he witnesses is his own surrender? This is the only way her mysteries make sense. Triangle. Circle. Square. Circle.

xix.

Before Martyn became a painter, he lived as a 14th-century troubadour. He stood below second-floor casements—serenading window panes with breakable melodies. He wore a sapphire tabard, and kept roses in a cloth sack over his shoulder in case of emergencies. Only two further objects accompanied him as he travelled the length of the land—his harp and a cake of soap. And he lived by filching from farms while he passed through strangers' fields at night like some kind of spectre. As for his music, a congregation of one would have been enough. He stood in walled gardens and threw his high, shy voice over rooftops. He sang songs like grappling hooks that scrambled across mediaeval thatch. Lyrics were there to be carolled and damsels there to rouse from endless slumber. At night, he dreamed under the fires of hopeful stars. But Martyn's voice at first was thin as yarn—too weak to bear the weight of a man's innate desire. For several days, he tried living exclusively on a diet of lemon juice and figs—to see if he became light enough to lift more easily. Lemon juice and figs—for as long as the yarn wouldn't thicken.

XX.

A numb fog has descended again—rendering all a shade of paint-water. And somewhere ahead unseen, the void awaits—a crevasse in an ice-sheet. Wild, unfathomable and deep, it would plunge him into bottomless darkness, even though he longs for light—he could drop a stone in and never hear it land.

xxi.

He remains grateful that what in normal employment are considered severe behavioural defects—extreme rages coupled with hypersensitive reactions towards others—a deadly hunger for prolonged spells without human interaction—a need to stare obsessively at people's faces—are considered core ingredients in the Person Specification of the Artist.

xxii.

If only he were a little bit more *woman*, Martyn thinks, it might bring him even closer to Anja—as a man he lacks answers to the question she poses. After yoga at Loudwater Farm by the swing-seat, they could sip vanilla chai tea, surfing Google images and purring at blurred snaps of Jake Gyllenhaal, the *ur*-text over which they'd collude in mischiefs self-inflicted after dark. They'd visit *Muse*, splurge on new dungarees, and he'd advise Anja on her choices, woman to woman, volunteering as a human clothes hanger as she modelled her outfits privately in the too-small cubicle. Not all would be perfect as a woman, true—there'd be devil in the particulars of arrangements. But they'd relish tender moments beneath duvets while undertaking *Mad Men* binges, and Rob would have no right to obstruct their evolving bond— an undarkening doorway to a sisterhood of intuitions.

xxiii.

Martyn lies on Anja's sofa—he's a boy being nursed back to full-strength from a gash in his thigh—inside the nave of Our Lady Help of Christians, where pools of sallow candlelight shimmer along walls. Rob is a bald priest swinging the thurible. Incense wafts over the pews. Anja gently strokes Martyn's head, and feeds him chicken soup. She's stroking too passionately—and he enjoys it too much—then Rob is next to the bed, egging her on while she hexes Martyn with the sign of the cross. A cock crows three times. Everything slows. The sofa lifts through the roof and Martyn sees the church resting on an island in the middle of Bury Lake—a flotilla of sailing vessels circling, each steered by a different imaginary ex-girlfriend dressed in a choirboy's cassock—and everyone holding a compact mirror pointed towards him, chanting *Spem in Alium*. On the church wall, monstrous fantasies play out in shadows. At last he wakes—in his own room. He doesn't know if he dreamt from fear or longing. He has to spend the whole day painting memento mori—just to calm down.

xxiv.

The angle is wrong. Someone's been reading his diary. Someone—he is sure—has dislodged it even as it hides in the nest of his cupboard. Is it Anja? Rob? By what kind of witchcraft did they find it? With a wince, he plucks a fine hair from his chest, and spreads it across the join of the slatted doors. The daily checks begin.

xxv.

Anja is with him for support—during his assessment at Shrodells Unit. He ought not to be fazed by these questions—he's faced down their like before with Anja at his side. Except, this time, he's forgotten his prepared responses. Anja's glances of compassion bewilder him. He sees the questions coming at him from a distance like high-speed trains—and the doctor is silent now, waiting for answers. An adolescent juggler hides inside Martyn's body—lobbing carving knives—and the knives are spinning round—scraping his innards—wanting to break out.

xxvi.

He knows Rob thinks he's a failure as a person—but their friendship is surely based on aesthetic evaluation of his output. Martyn is essentially noble—it's only the mechanisms of the market that have sullied his career and personality. Once he's served his artistic time underground, he will reap commercial reward. And just like Rob's doctor, lecturer, and lawyer friends, a maverick-creative counts as a valuable addition to Rob's friendship portfolio, carefully placed among the supporting cast—like an over-the-shoulder roast-vegetable option at a banquet—would Sir enjoy carrot, or parsnip perhaps?

xxvii.

Off-limits, unsolvable—maybe Anja should be thrust from his life for good this time. But how can he escape her? He's gripped by something he can't grasp. Her thighs are like two slender willows at the edge of the Chess. As soon as he's fled from the murmuring river, those same legs will chase him all summer down stony paths. Every time he rounds a new bend, searching for sanctuary in that flooded gravel-pit wilderness, she'll be there, tapping his shoulder—with the branch of one arm—and he'll hesitate—while she caresses his body with silvery leaves.

xxviii.

Rickmansworth Week, the annual canal festival, and Martyn is skimming the blurb: this valley lassoed by the M25 at the edge of the London sprawl—where Colne, Chess, and Gade converge. The basin-like shape of the frost hollow—site of England's largest ever daily temperature range—still clings to its ongoing record. It seems apt to Martyn that if his home has achieved an English fame, it's by virtue of a kind of excess weather.

xxix.

Sleepless at midnight—but not wondering about Rob and Anja lying in bed in the dark, somewhere else in Rickmansworth. Not thinking about Anja awake on her side, her abdomen pressed close to Rob's—listening to him sleeping—feeling his tanned and sculpted limbs move—sensing the glow of his body heat. Not thinking about her longing to be held—longing to stroke Rob awake.

xxx.

Every portrait of Martyn's seems a self-portrait; every weather-beaten Lake landscape his own disturbed consciousness; his studies of Maple Lodge sewage works reek of his own rot. He fears he belongs to the paintings more than they belong to him— what happened to the Martyn that he used to know and half-love? If he's attentive, he finds he's scattered everywhere— dispersed through the gloop of oils into no more than brushwork and the reflection of light. The paintings seem to be painting themselves, proliferating, mutating. He watches the paint—in his latest still-life interior—drip down the brush, trickle along the length of his wrist, staining his skin.

xxxi.

Sometimes Anja praises Martyn so highly she makes him feel like Superman. He has the Superman dream always the same way: not the caped crusader saving the civilised world, but Clark Kent the reporter wearing preppy spectacles and befuddled by Lois Lane—except Lois is Anja—and Anja's nipples are made of kryptonite. But this is a dream and Lois-Anja is also somehow Lex Luthor at one and the same time—looking like Gene Hackman with his big-collared 1970s shirt—and Lois-Anja Hackman takes off Clark Kent's glasses, kisses his brow sadly, then draws his head closer to her deadly, trembling chest.

xxxii.

That particular way Rob has of making Martyn grind his incisors—when Rob's voice cracks from stress into two pitches at once. And the throb he inserts behind Martyn's eyelids when his Doc Martens stomp over the floorboards of Anja's living room—stamping all over Martyn as he lies on the sofa listening—until Martyn's head feels like a melon that's been dropped from a skyscraper. Yes, that.

xxxiii.

Martyn presses *Send*—retreats to his burrow—and watches his rabid lust for Anja subside. Poor Rob—the man acknowledges no subplots. *Eat me, Anja, eat me.* Now Martyn waits for a currant cake to appear before his eyes—inside its little glass box. He waits. And waits.

xxxiv.

Talking to Anja is sometimes strange—but no, he can't hate her for that. His view through the window is clear—then there is a splintering. He finds himself with a mouth full of shattered glass—and yet he keeps chewing.

XXXV.

Life breaks you apart slowly—with every relationship, the miniature sculptor works her hammer and chisel on the stone lump of your heart. If you're really lucky, Martyn thinks, a man survives well enough to be left in the end with something recognisable—maybe not a work of art but something you can live with. It takes a lot of false starts for a sculptor to shape a stone well—if she taps the surface a touch too hard, she finds a fault line waiting.

xxxvi.

Martyn's brain is floating somewhere in a bottle of gin—he's been hauled to Rileys in Watford to play snooker with Rob and Anja. There are green rectangles in lines everywhere—like he's playing in an endless hall of mirrors that stinks of beer and sweat—and Rob is wiping the grubby floor with Martyn. He's on the last black, playing a trick shot behind his back with his right leg balanced in the air—and Anja is doubled up laughing. Rob might as well be picking him up and rubbing his face into Anja's breasts saying *This is what you could have, Kent—if you could only fly*. And he knows he ought to embrace it all and just ruffle Rob's hair with a fond palm—but really he wants to clamp Rob's head in an arm lock and smash the fucker's teeth out of his mouth. Today he wants the game to be over. He picks up the snooker cue, gripping it hard in both hands.

Notes

p.5, E.M. Forster, *Howards End* (1910) (London: Penguin English Library, 2012), p.195.

p.6, from Paul Farley and Michael Symmons Roberts, *Edgelands: Journeys into England's True Wilderness* (London: Jonathan Cape, 2011), p.10. The concept of part-rural, part-urban 'edgelands' was first described by the geographer Marion Shoard in her essay 'Edgelands', in *Remaking the Landscape*, Jennifer Jenkins (ed.), (Profile Books, 2002).

p.17, found prose: list of side-effects taken from leaflet for Atenolol, a medication for treating high blood pressure.

p.23, material adapted from Three Rivers Museum leaflet –Feargus O'Connor (TRMT Publications, 2004)

p.25, material adapted from Marvel Top Trumps Super Heroes Card Game (Marvel Comics International Ltd., 1977)

p.65, 'Chewing Glass: xv.' is a version of *The Odyssey*, Book 6, ll. 127-137.

p.69, cf. Katherine Gallagher: 'an audience of one is enough', in her poem 'Entente', from *Circus Apprentice* (Todmorden: Arc Publications, 2006).

V.

Acknowledgements

Grateful acknowledgement is made to the editors of the following magazines and anthologies, in which many of these pieces (or versions of them) appeared: *All the Sins; Cease, Cows; Envoi; Flash: The International Short-Short Story Magazine; Flash Fiction Festival, One; Flash Frontier; The Forge Literary Magazine; Funny Bone: Flashing for Comic Relief; Ink, Sweat & Tears; Nutshells and Nuggets; Orbis; Poem; Prole; Spelk; Stand; Strange Poetry.*

In the process of writing this book, I benefited from feedback and guidance from a number of writers and tutors whose contributions were crucial to the final text: in particular Fiona Sampson, my M.A. supervisor at Kingston University, who helped me to get the initial idea off the ground, and Patricia Debney, whose comments and advice at a later stage in the project were extremely valuable. I am greatly indebted to the support of my Southbank writers group – Helen Turnbull, John Mackay, John Riglin, Sharon Stead and Stuart Bird – who kept me going with both companionship and detailed editorial suggestions when the manuscript seemed lost. Thanks too to Robin Thomas for the same reasons. I would also like to thank Bernadine Evaristo and Maggie Gee from The Arvon Foundation's 2015 Totleigh Barton Fiction Retreat; Beth Harris and David Cundall for research suggestions; James Coleman, for helpful feedback; Amie Caddy, Helena Nelson, James Byrne, Paul Perry, Robert Vas Dias, Steven Timberman, and Tiffany Anne Tondut for comments on early versions of parts of the manuscript; and my partner Lynda for her advice, patience and tolerant support of my obsession with writing. Lastly, thanks to Sarah Leavesley of V. Press, for having faith in the manuscript as the press's first full book of flash fiction.

V.

Earlier Publications:

All the Sins: Cause for Alarm: xii. Good Neighbours Make Good Fences
https://allthesins.co.uk/issues-2/issue-2-movement/good-neighbours-make-good-fences-mike-loveday/

Cease, Cows: Cause for Alarm: v. Don't Sweat the Small Stuff, as 'The Second Shed'
http://ceasecows.com/2016/11/14/the-second-shed-by-michael-loveday/

Envoi: Issue 173, June 2016: The Invisible World: iii. The Chess, March

Flash: The International Short-Short Story Magazine: Vol.8, No.1 (April 2015); Vol.8, No.2 (October 2015), Vol.9, No.1 (April 2016): Cause for Alarm: i. Lost Object, as 'Gorgeous'; The Invisible World: ix. Town Ditch, September, as 'Town Ditch'; Chewing Glass: iv., as 'Shopping'

Flash Fiction Festival, One (Ad Hoc Fiction, 2017): Chewing Glass; xviii.

Flash Frontier: Cause for Alarm: iv. The Other Denholm
http://www.flash-frontier.com/november-2016-birds/#denholm

The Forge Literary Magazine: Chewing Glass: i.-iii., v., vii., ix-xiii., xvii., xix.-xxi., xxiii., xxv.-xxvi., xxix.-xxxi., xxxiii.-xxxvi.
https://www.forgelitmag.com/flm/2017/05/29/chewing-glass/

Funny Bone: Flashing for Comic Relief (Flash: the International Short-Short Story Press, 2017): Chewing Glass: xxx., as 'Kryptonite'

Ink, Sweat & Tears: Cause for Alarm: iii. PG Certificate
http://www.inksweatandtears.co.uk/pages//?s=michael+loveday

Nutshells and Nuggets: The Invisible World: x. Batchworth Lake, October
https://nutshellsandnuggets.tumblr.com/post/157981020217/michael-loveday-one-poem

Orbis: Issue 177, Autumn 2016: Cause for Alarm: ii. Denholm Is Relying on Several Handsets for Incoming Calls, Each with a Separate Telephone Line

Poem: Vol. 4, Number 2, June 2016: The Invisible World: vii.

V.

Batchworth Lake, July; The Invisible World: xii. Stockers Lock, December

Prole: Issue 25, April 2018: Cause for Alarm: xiii. Onion Skin

Spelk: Cause for Alarm: xvi. Solitary Man, Or How He Tries to Save Himself, at 4:59 p.m. on Sunday the 13th May, with the Words of the Brooklyn Cowboy, Neil Diamond
https://spelkfiction.com/2017/03/17/solitary-man-or-how-he-is-saved-at-504-p-m-on-sunday-the-14th-april-by-the-brooklyn-cowboy-neil-diamond/

Stand: Volume 12 (3), 203: Cause for Alarm: xv. Alarm

Strange Poetry: Cause for Alarm: vii. The Small Print
https://strange-poetry.com/2017/06/06/michael-loveday-the-small-print/

V.

V.

Michael Loveday was born in Wembley, and spent over thirty years living on the Northwest edge of London, including nine years in Rickmansworth in the Three Rivers District of Hertfordshire. Despite the coincidence of his birthplace, his skills were strangely overlooked by a succession of England football managers. At the age of 29, to mask his disappointment, he took up writing. His debut poetry pamphlet *He Said / She Said* was published by Happen*Stance* Press in 2011. Since 2013, he has been working as a tutor in Community and Higher Education, teaching fiction, poetry, life writing and general literature. In 2016, he moved to Bath. He is a Director of the National Association of Writers in Education, and his blog of interviews with writers of flash fiction, poetry and prose poetry can be found at pagechatter.org. *Three Men on the Edge* was inspired by his experiences of an in-between place.

V.